Developing Lite
POETRY

READING AND WRITING
ACTIVITIES FOR THE LITERACY HOUR

year

Christine Moorcroft

Series consultant:

Ray Barker

A & C BLACK

Contents

Poetic forms

Theme and meaning

Acknowledgements
The author and publishers are grateful for permission to reproduce the following:
p. 12 'The Visitor' reproduced by permission of Anne Serraillier; p. 19 'Eye Sore' reprinted by permission of PFD on behalf of Roger McGough © Roger McGough 1983; p. 22 'Eletelephony' from *Tirra Lirra* by Laura E. Richards. Copyright © 1930, 1932 by Laura E. Richards, copyright © 1960 by Hamilton E. Richards. By permission of Little, Brown and Company (Inc.); p. 23 'The Snitterjipe' © James Reeves from *Complete Poems for Children* (Heinemann). Reprinted by permission of the James Reeves Estate; p. 26 'Leisure' by W. H. Davies Reproduced with permission of Mr K. P. Griffin on behalf of the Will Trust of Mrs H.M. Davies; p. 32 'Song of the Street' Poems and melodies from Iceland, CD, published by Torfi Ólafson, 1997); p. 33 'Haiku (Ice on the Front Step)' © Patricia V Dawson. Reproduced with permission of Maria Dawson and Patricia V. Dawson; p. 35 'Silver Aeroplane' © 2000 John Foster from *The Works*, compiled by Paul Cookson (Macmillan) included by permission of the author; p. 37 'Dust' © 1979 John Mole. First published in *Once there were Dragons* (Andre Deutsch); p. 38 'The Owl and the Astronaut' © Gareth Owen 2000. Reproduced with permission of the author c/o Rogers Coleridge & White Ltd., 20 Powis Mews, London W11 1JN; p. 44 'They're Fetching in Ivy and Holly' © Charles Causley, from *Collected Poems for Children*, published by Macmillan. Reproduced with permission of David Higham Associates ; p. 45 'In This City' © Alan Brownjohn 1961; p. 46 Two limericks reproduced with permission of A. P. Watt on behalf of the Earl of Oxford and Asquith, (*The Reader's Digest Book of Facts*, 1985)

Every effort has been made to trace copyright holders and to obtain their permission for use of copyright material. The author and publishers would be pleased to rectify in future editions any error or omission.

Reprinted 2002, 2003 Published 2001 by A & C Black Publishers Limited, 37 Soho Square, London W1D 3QZ www.acblack.com

ISBN 0-7136-5874-6

Copyright: text © Christine Moorcroft, 2001; illustrations © Bridget Dowty, 2001; cover illustration © Alison Dexter, 2001

The authors and publisher would like to thank Ray Barker, Madeleine Madden, Kim Pérez and Julia Tappin for their advice in producing this series of books.

A CIP catalogue record for this book is available from the British Library.

A & C Black uses paper produced with elemental chlorine-free pulp, harvested from managed sustainable forests.
Printed in Great Britain by Caligraving Ltd, Thetford, Norfolk.

Developing Literacy: Poetry is a series of seven photocopiable activity books for the Literacy Hour. Each book provides a range of poetry activities that support the teaching of reading and writing skills at text, sentence and word levels. They contain more than enough lesson ideas for the year for which they are intended, and provide teachers with a selection of activities to choose from.

The activities are designed to be carried out in the time allocated to independent work and incorporate strategies to encourage independent learning – for example, ways in which children can evaluate their own work or that of a partner.

The activities in Year 6 encourage children to:

- develop their enjoyment of different kinds of poems, including classic and modern poetry; the work of long-established poets, poets from different cultures and times; and poetry in different forms, such as limerick, riddle, cinquain, haiku, tanka, conversation, monologue, letter, diary, free verse and nonsense poetry;

- develop their skills in analysing poetry and comparing the styles of poets, past and present;

- enjoy, investigate and create humour through word-play, ambiguity, rhyme and play on meanings;

- explore the quality of sounds produced by rhythm and different forms of rhyme and assonance;

- explore the use of similes, comparisons, metaphors, kennings and figurative language;

- investigate the language of poetry from the past;

- use poems they have read as models for their own writing.

The National Literacy Strategy and poetry

The National Literacy Strategy *Framework for Teaching* encourages teachers to read all kinds of poetry and verse with children, including playground chants, nursery rhymes, action rhymes, advertisements and jingles as well as more formal poetry. The text-level objectives include teaching *about* poetry – different types of poetry, the devices used by poets, the 'messages' of poems and even the shapes of poems, plus many of the technical terms associated with poetry. Research also indicates that the ability to appreciate rhyme and rhythm has a positive effect on children's learning to read and spell.

Several word-level objectives can thus be successfully taught *through* poetry: the use of rhyme to teach about phonics and onset and rime, and of rhythm to teach about syllables.

However, teachers should not lose sight of the fun of poetry – the 'playing with words' of poets like Roger McGough and the clever use of humour by poets like Charles Causley and E V Rieu. In poetry, children can ignore the rules of grammar and put words together in new ways. And, as with other kinds of writing, the children can learn from experts. The teacher's role is to help the children to recognise a particular form of poetry, to provide a structure to help them to write it, and to help them to identify the devices used by poets, practise them and use them in their own poems.

Planning a poem

These headings could be written on a board or flip chart to focus the children's thoughts when they are planning a poem:

Title

Theme

Type of poem (For example: action rhyme, jingle, nursery rhyme, lullaby, story, riddle, tongue-twister, observation, performance, humorous, epitaph, conversation, prayer or ballad.)

Form (For example: shape poem, haiku, tanka, cinquain, couplet, list, rhyme, free verse or limerick.)

Poetic devices (For example: metaphor, simile, personification, kenning and so on.)

Sound (What kind of rhythm should your poem have? Fast, slow, marching, walking, strolling, meandering, jumping, skipping, singing or chatting?)

Rhyme (Will it rhyme? How will it rhyme? For example: full rhyme, half-rhyme, internal rhyme, ends of words, middles of words, consecutive lines or alternate lines.)

Other sound devices (For example: onomatopoeia, alliteration or assonance.)

Using poetry in the Literacy Hour

This book focuses on the independent part of the Literacy Hour but the notes on pages 6–8 and at the foot of each activity page suggest a variety of ways in which you can introduce poetry lessons, present whole-class activities and use plenary sessions to conclude the lessons. Teachers will find it useful to vary their approaches, and could also try some of the following, as appropriate for their year group:

- playing professional tape recordings of poems;
- choral speaking by individuals, small or large groups, and the whole class;
- learning poems a line or two at a time (varying the tone and expression as appropriate);
- reciting poems which have been learned;
- enacting, miming or singing poems;
- listing rhymes, alliterative or onomatopoeic words;
- clapping, tapping or stamping rhythms and even moving the whole body (jumping, walking and so on);
- making lists of words on a topic;
- composing poems as a group or class;
- holding small-group discussions and open forums during which the children discuss poems they have read or written.

Listening to poems

Listening to the poets themselves or actors reading aloud can be of special value in helping the children to enjoy a poem. At the same time, the children learn how to read poetry aloud themselves. School television programmes on poetry could be used, as could commercially available tapes: for example *Poetry Please* and *The Nation's Favourite Poems* (BBC) or *The Penguin Book of English Verse* (Penguin Classics).

Reading poems aloud

Several activities in this book ask the children to read poems aloud (both their own and those of other poets). This helps them to appreciate the poem's meaning, atmosphere and rhythm; and in the case of their own poems, to think of changes which might improve them. Sometimes, the notes which accompany an activity suggest ways in which the poems can be read aloud (for example, individuals, pairs,

or groups can read the parts of different characters, or read individual lines, groups of lines, verses and choruses). The way in which a poem is spoken can make a valuable contribution to the children's understanding, appreciation and enjoyment of it. Experiment with different methods: for example, a poem with a quiet atmosphere might be spoken using a combination of solo voices and hushed combined voices; the rhythm of a train might be created by having one group beginning to read a line while another group is finishing the previous line.

Memorising poems

Many of the activities in this book suggest that the children memorise a poem, rhyme or verse. When they memorise poetry, the children increase their vocabulary and develop the skill of using it expressively; they build up a rich store of creative ways in which words can be used, and they begin to use them themselves.

To help the children to memorise a poem, read it aloud to them, then repeat it, encouraging them to join in. Either display an enlarged copy of the poem, or work with a small group of children who each have their own copy to follow. Read a line, then cover it and ask the children to repeat it, gradually building up the number of lines covered, until the children can recite the entire poem.

Organisation

None of the activities requires much in the way of additional resources besides scissors, glue, word-banks and simple dictionaries. Other materials are specified in the teachers' notes on the pages.

Extension activities

Most of the activity sheets end with a challenge (**Now try this!**) which reinforces and extends the children's learning and provides the teacher with an opportunity for assessment. These more challenging activities might be appropriate for only a few children; it is not expected that the whole class should complete all of them. On some pages there is space for the children to complete the extension activities, but others will require a notebook or separate sheet of paper.

Notes on the activities

The notes below expand upon those provided at the foot of each activity page. They give ideas and suggestions for making the most of the activity sheet, including suggestions for the whole-class introduction, the plenary session or for follow-up work using an adapted version of the activity sheet. To help teachers to select appropriate learning experiences for their pupils, the activities are grouped into sections within each book, but the pages need not be presented in the order in which they appear, unless otherwise stated.

Reading aloud

This section encourages the children to consider the effects of poets' language and the way in which poets can suggest, by their choice of words and by the details they give, the tone of voice in which a poem should be read. It helps the children to develop skills in reading aloud.

Wot a marf (page 9) develops the children's appreciation of the ways in which people's speech can be represented in poetry by unconventional spellings. The exercise is to show how the poem is *enriched* by the use of non-standard English.

The poem in **A poem from an antique land** (page 10) should be read in a grand and bold manner, expressing the conviction that the speaker thinks he is mightier than other people, has no fear of them and expects them to admire him. Lines 10–14 express irony: the 'works' of Ozymandias (Pharoah Ramses II) were ruined and disappeared long ago.

Words on a pedestal (page 11) develops skills in writing concisely to create an impression. Discussion will help the children to come up with a statement which conveys their chosen person's character.

In **Conversation poem: 1** (page 12) the children use their voices to represent different speakers and the narrator and to show the speakers' feelings. Discuss the way in which the feelings of the woman and her husband change (and can be shown by tone of voice). Point out the sudden change of tone in the poem: the skeleton clattered downhill and 'all was still'.

In **Conversation poem: 2** (page 13) the children write a story poem told in the form of a conversation; their poems can be modelled on the structure of *The Visitor* (page 12) but could tell *any* kind of story. If they follow the rhyme structure of *The Visitor*, discourage them from allowing rhyme to become the main issue: the important thing is to tell the story as a conversation with a good rhythm.

Monologue reader (page 14) develops skills in reading aloud to express a single speaker's character, feelings and attitudes. Grace Nichols is from Guyana: the children should notice that the spellings of the words represent the Afro-Caribbean English dialect and accent. *Answers*: **rhythm**: chant (the poem is a rap); **speed**: fast; **main rhyming sound**: 'oo' (point out the half-rhyme 'ow'); **pauses between verses**: short (there are no full stops); the last line sounds as if there is more to come ('mek me tell you' … what?): it has no full stop.

The effects of words

The activities in this section develop the children's understanding of the devices which poets use and the ways in which they convey meaning by their choice of words. They also develop the children's skills in working with rhyme, alliteration and other effects, and in selecting words to convey feelings or impressions.

Verbs with verve (page 15) develops appreciation of shades of meaning of verbs. *Answers*: 1 glittering (*A Winter Night* by William Barnes); 2 charging (*From a Railway Carriage* by Robert Louis Stevenson); 3 drifts (*The Old Men Admiring Themselves in the Water* by W. B. Yeats); 4 peered, 5 breathed, 6 bursts (*The Rime of the Ancient Mariner* by Samuel Taylor Coleridge); 7 sprang (*The Wind in a Frolic* by William Howitt); 8 loiter (*Goblin Market* by Christina Rossetti); 9 swirling (*Why Does It Snow?* by Laura E. Richards).

Adverbs alive (page 16) develops appreciation of the ways in which adverbs can be used to create atmosphere. The children should notice the sounds of the adverbs in this poem as well as their meanings: they are all soft-sounding words. *Answers*: (secretly) 'stealthily'; (without force) 'gently'; (without stopping) 'perpetually' and 'incessantly'; (not fixed to the ground) 'loosely'; (without a sound) 'silently', 'softly'. Alliteration: 'loosely lying', 'silently sifting'; assonance: 'stealthily', 'perpetually', 'settling'.

A house awakes (page 17) introduces personification. The introductory session or a guided writing activity could include a discussion of the sounds and actions of objects such as garage doors, locks, lights, gutters, gratings, taps, heating, plumbing, kettles and alarm clocks. They might moan, groan, complain, growl, blink, gargle, swallow, shiver or scream.

Figurative language (page 18) consolidates the children's appreciation of figurative language and encourages them to explore ways in which they can enrich their own writing. Comparisons and similes: 'round as a pillow', 'whiter than milk', 'softer than if it were covered in silk', 'like men in a battle'; metaphors: 'growls as if he would fix his claws'; personification: 'What way does *he* go?' '*he* rides', '*his* sounding flight'.

Word-play (page 19) presents a very short poem (of just one sentence) which uses the homophones saw/soar/sore to express an idea about a tall building. It also plays on the ambiguity of 'eyesore' (a sore eye or an ugly sight).

Inventing words (page 20) encourages the children to investigate the ways in which poets combine words in unexpected ways, sometimes linking them to make new words, and even inventing words to convey impressions.

Kennings (page 21) could be linked with word-level work on word-derivations: the children are likely to come across many words of Old Norse origin which have come from kennings. *Answers*: 11 skyscraper; 12 clothes horse; 13 gold-digger; 14 joy-rider.

Nonsense words (page 22) develops the children's appreciation of the ways in which words can be combined for their humorous effects.

In **The unknown** (page 23) the children investigate the ways in which the poet creates an air of mystery, partly by describing parts of the Snitterjipe and evidence of his presence – the whole creature is never seen.

Atmosphere: 1 (page 24) helps the children to appreciate the ways in which poets use words to create a mood or atmosphere. *Suggested answers*: the weather is hot and humid and there is not a breath of wind (introduce the word 'oppressive'); the mood is one of sluggishness – it is too hot for movement; the bird longs for a refreshing shower of rain; the creatures are hardly moving except to try to find shady cool places. In the extension activity the children should notice the contrast between the still, oppressive heat and the splashing of the bird in the cooling stream.

Atmosphere: 2 (page 25) provides a poem whose atmosphere can be compared with that of *Noon* (page 24). The atmosphere of this poem is also still and quiet but, unlike in *Noon*, there is a feeling of expectation. It is about a cricket match in which the last player is about to bat. There is a 'breathless hush' because victory depends on his performance. The poem encourages the reader to support the batting team, because it is presented from their point of view.

Rhythm and rhyme: 1 (page 26) develops the children's ability to appreciate the effect of the rhythm and pace of a poem. The regular, smooth rhythm of this poem and its slow pace create a peaceful atmosphere which reflects the value the poet places on leisure.

In **Rhythm and rhyme: 2** and **3** (pages 27–28) the children explore another poem with a noticeable rhythm. They should notice the repetition of certain lines. This repetition evokes the surging charge of the men in battle; it is as if the charge goes on and on throughout the poem. The change in rhythm in verses 1 to 5 comes at lines 7, 16, 24, 37 and 48 respectively. It separates the description of the action from the poet's reflections on the event. It begins with a regular rhythm of 'galloping horses' and then begins to stumble, as the horses did in battle.

Assonance game: 1 and **2** (pages 29–30) develops the children's skills in recognising and using assonance. The words on page 30 could be masked to make blank cards on which the children can write other words with assonance.

All in a word (page 31) develops the children's appreciation of the connotations of words.

Poetic forms

This section introduces some of the forms in which poems can be written and provides structures to help the children to write their own poems.

Free verse (page 32) is a translation of a modern Icelandic poem. The activity develops the children's appreciation of the way in which free verse can be used to create an atmosphere and express a mood or feeling. The irregular rhythm reflects the subject matter – of someone wandering, without any set purpose, through urban streets. Words which help to create the mood of loneliness are: 'emptiness', 'no life', 'no sound', 'not a withering leaf', 'nothing'. In the extension activity, the negative words which the children should have underlined are: 'no' (lines 4 and 5), 'not' (lines 6 and 7) and 'nothing' (lines 8 and 12).

Haiku and **Haiku day** (pages 33–34) consolidate the children's appreciation of the structure and essence of a haiku and provide a structure to help the children write their own haiku series about the events of a day.

Tanka (page 35) consolidates the children's appreciation of the structure and essence of a tanka . A tanka has five lines. It is a haiku with two extra lines and a syllable pattern of 5,7,5,7,7. A tanka is a poem which captures the essence of a moment in time, for example, a bird landing on a branch, a gust of wind, someone hearing good news, or a flash of lightning.

In **Wishing cinquains** (page 36) the children revise their previous learning about cinquains and write their own cinquain about a wish. Point out the syllable pattern 2, 4, 6, 8, 2. It is as if the syllable pattern 'snaps' back to two, like an elastic band.

What am I? (page 37) encourages the children to think of a riddle as a series of clues which lead the reader to the answer. It develops their appreciation of 'play on words': for example, 'gathering of dusk'/'gathering of dust'. The extension activity invites the children to incorporate figures of speech into their own riddles.

Parody (page 38) develops the children's understanding of the ways in which poets create humour through imitating and altering existing poems. They should notice that the basic rhythm and rhyme-pattern of *The Owl and the Pussy-Cat* is retained although the lengths of the lines and the number of lines in the verse have been changed.

Limerick rhyme patterns (page 39) consolidates the children's appreciation of limericks.

Theme and meaning

This section concentrates on the subjects or themes of poems, the styles of individual poets, the ways in which a poet's experience and culture are expressed in poems and the ways in which poets convey a message. There are opportunities for the children to examine the work of poets (both past and contemporary). The children are also encouraged to investigate and enjoy the ways in which humour can be created in poetry.

Sounds funny: 1 (page 40) presents a poem whose humour depends on the similarity of sound between words for vegetables, fruits and other plants and other words. *Answers*: care at, beats, turned up, reddish, can't elope, let us, we'd, pair; fir, plane, oak, rowan, willow, ash, leaf.

Sounds funny: 2 (page 41) introduces the humour of 'spoonerisms' and encourages the children to make up some of their own. *Answers*: 1 poured with rain; 2 stuck in the mud; 3 as keen as mustard; 4 reading books; 5 let sleeping dogs lie; 6 square meals. Shopping list: a mound of peat, a pan of cares, a bin of teens, bellyjeans, keys and parrots, fates and digs, pick cheese, fleet wakes.

Symbol fun (page 42) encourages the children to explore the humour which can be created by using letters, numbers and symbols to represent phonemes and words. The children could word-process other 'symbol fun' ideas and explore text message symbols on mobile phones. *Answers*: t, slap-, 2 late, 1ce, 4tify, rel8, fran ✔, 10tacle, 4tune, -ing, like a • a g8, a l8 ✳ter, £ded, ✳vation, Sw1C, aX✔, Icel&, p&a

Playing with meanings (page 43) encourages the children to explore the creation of humour through word-association and similar-sounding words. The title of the poem plays on words (a case could contain fish; it is also an action in court). *Answers*: 'battery' is the crime of harming someone physically, fish are 'battered'; monkfish is a fish and a monk is a member of a religious order; 'cod' sounds like 'God', 'So help me God' is an oath sworn in court; soles are fish, 'souls' are people (explain the figure of speech 'lost souls'); 'crabby' means bad-tempered, crabs are sea-creatures; 'plaice' is a fish and sounds like 'place'; whiting is a fish and sounds similar to 'writing'; skate is a fish, 'bored' sounds like 'board' ('skateboard'); scampi are shellfish and start with a similar sound to 'scamper'; congers are eels, congas are dances; 'wrapped up' means 'completed', fish are sold wrapped up in newspaper.

Analysing a poem (page 44) presents a poem written as if by a cat observing Christmas preparations. The humour arises from the questioning of popular Christmas rituals.

Layers of meaning (page 45) provides a challenging poem with a literal meaning and a deeper meaning.

Linked by a letter (page 46) provides an example of linked poems (one gives a response to the other) and an example of a poem (here a limerick) in the form of a letter.

A poem from the past (page 47) invites the children to explore the original language of an Elizabethan poem. Reading it aloud and listening carefully to the words should help them to work out what they mean. *Answers*: 'Mutabilitie' means an ability to change. Changed spellings: 'plentious' (plenteous), 'banisht' (banished), 'eares' (ears), 'corne' (corn), 'holde' (hold), 'reape' (reap), 'Faerie' (Fairy). Words used differently or no longer used: 'full' (very), 'to-fore' (until then), 'oft' (often), 'enrold' (rolled), 'yold' (yielded).

The past tenses are banisht (banished), enrold (enrolled, but meaning 'rolled') and yold (yielded). Examples of archaic word-order are: 'oft him pinched sore', 'he did holde'.

A poet's style (page 48) is a framework to support the children's analysis of a poet's style.

Wot a marf

- **Read the poem aloud.**
- **Underline the words and phrases in the poem which are not** standard English **.**
- **Write the poem in standard English.**

_____

_____

_____

_____

_____

_____

_____

_____

_____

_____

Epitaph on a 'Marf'

Wot a marf 'e'd got,
Wot a marf.
When 'e was a kid,
Goo' Lor' luv'll
'Is pore old muvver
Must 'a' fed 'im wiv a shuvvle.

Wot a gap 'e'd got,
Pore chap,
'E'd never been known to larf,
'Cos if 'e did
It's a penny to a quid
'E'd 'a' split 'is fice in 'arf.

Anonymous

- **Read your standard English version aloud. What has been lost by changing the poem?** _____

_____

_____

- **Re-write the poem in another dialect and accent you know.**

You can use dialect and slang words, and change the spellings of words to show the accent.

Teachers' note Read the poem aloud and ask the children if they recognise the accent and dialect from which it comes. Encourage them to say any words which they cannot understand and to work out what they mean. This is a poem which they can practise reading aloud for a class recital.

Developing Literacy
Poetry Year 6
© A & C Black

A poem from an antique land

Ozymandias was the Egyptian pharoah, Ramses II.

- **What do the words on the ruined sculpture tell you about Ozymandias?**

MY NAME IS OZYMANDIAS KING OF KINGS LOOK ON MY WORKS, YE MIGHTY, AND DESPAIR!

_____

_____

_____

_____

_____

- **Underline the words in this poem which tell you about the character of Ozymandias.**

- **Write a short character study of Ozymandias. Use words from the poem to support what you say.**

Ozymandias

I met a traveller from an antique land,
Who said: Two vast and trunkless legs of stone
Stand in the desert. Near them, on the sand,
Half sunk, a shattered visage lies, whose frown
And wrinkled lip and sneer of cold command,
Tell that its sculptor well those passions read,
Which yet survive stamped on these lifeless things,
The hand that mocked them, and the heart that fed:
And on the pedestal these words appear:
'My name is Ozymandias, King of Kings:
Look on my works, ye Mighty, and despair!'
Nothing beside remains. Round the decay
Of that colossal wreck, boundless and bare
The lone and level sands stretch far away.

Percy Bysshe Shelley

Now try this!

- **What do the last three lines tell you about Ozymandias' power?**

Teachers' note After the first activity, the children could read the entire poem aloud in their group, one person reading the words of the poet, another the traveller and a third Ozymandias. In the extension activity, help the children to notice the irony in lines 10-14 (see **Introduction** page 6).

Developing Literacy Poetry Year 6 © A & C Black

Words on a pedestal

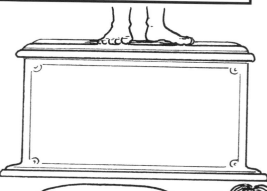

Imagine a statue of someone from history.

- On the pedestal write what that person might say about himself or herself.
- Plan a poem about the statue. Make notes.

Model your poem on *Ozymandias*.

The place where the statue stands

List what the statue might see.

The statue itself

Face and expression

The character of the dead person

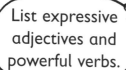
List expressive adjectives and powerful verbs.

Now try this!

- Write your poem and read it through. Make any changes which will improve it.
- Practise reading your poem aloud.

Teachers' note The children should first have completed page 10. Introduce the activity by discussing the impressions which can be created by a few words. Encourage the children to build up the impression they want to create about the person. During the plenary session they could read their poems aloud, using their voices to convey that impression.

Developing Literacy Poetry Year 6 © A & C Black

Conversation poem: 1

- **Practise reading the poem aloud.**
- **Make notes on how the spoken words should sound.**

surprised, interested

The Visitor

A crumbling churchyard, the sea and the moon;
The waves had gouged out grave and bone;
A man was walking, late and alone…

He saw a skeleton on the ground;
A ring on a bony hand he found.

He ran home to his wife and gave her the ring.
"Oh, where did you get it?" He said not a thing.

"It's the prettiest ring in the world," she said,
As it glowed on her finger. They skipped off to bed.

At midnight they woke. In the dark outside–
"Give me my ring!" a chill voice cried.

"What was that, William? What did it say?"
"Don't worry, my dear. It'll soon go away."

"I'm coming!" A skeleton opened the door.
"Give me my ring!" It was crossing the floor.

"What was that, William? What did it say?"
"Don't worry, my dear. It'll soon go away."

"I'm touching you now! I'm climbing the bed."
The wife pulled the sheet right over her head.

It was torn from her grasp and tossed in the air:
"I'll drag you out of your bed by the hair!"

"What was that, William? What did it say?"
"Throw the ring through the window!
THROW IT AWAY!"

She threw it. The skeleton leapt from the sill,
Scooped up the ring and clattered downhill,
Fainter… and fainter… Then all was still.

Ian Serraillier

- **Describe how the poet builds the tension in the poem.**

Teachers' note Read only the first two verses aloud and ask the children what kind of atmosphere they create. Invite the children to demonstrate the expressions with which different parts of it should be read and how they would read each different voice. They could first underline the words of each speaker and the narrator in different colours.

Developing Literacy
Poetry Year 6
© A & C Black

Conversation poem: 2

• **Plan a conversation poem to read aloud.** What happens?

Story summary		
Setting	**Atmosphere**	**Characters**

Notes

Opening

Conversation

Ending

• **Now write your poem.**

• **Read your poem aloud.**
• **Make any changes which will improve it.**
• **Practise reading the final version aloud.**

Teachers' note Use this with page 12. The children could first give a brief summary of the story of *The Visitor*. Their own conversation poem could tell a story they know. Ask them to give a brief summary of a short story the whole class knows, to identify the characters and narrator in it and to say how they would set the scene (in two verses) for this story.

Developing Literacy
Poetry Year 6
© A & C Black

Monologue reader

- Read the poem.
- Fill in the chart to show how the poem should be read aloud.

Rhythm	dance	☐
	walk	☐
	chant	☐
	trot	☐
Speed	slow	☐
	fast	☐
Main rhyming sound	oo	☐
	ed	☐
	ow	☐
	ing	☐

Underline the main rhymes in the poem.

Pauses between verses	very short	☐
	short	☐
	long	☐
	very long	☐

How can you tell from the punctuation?

Wha Me Mudder Do

Mek me tell you wha me Mudder do
wha me mudder do
wha me mudder do

Me mudder pound plantain mek fufu*
Me mudder catch crab mek calaloo* stew

Mek me tell you wha me mudder do
wha me mudder do
wha me mudder do

Me mudder beat hammer
Me mudder turn screw
she paint chair red
then she paint it blue

Mek me tell you wha me mudder do
wha me mudder do
wha me mudder do

Me mudder chase bad-cow
with one 'Shoo'
she paddle down river
in she own canoe
Ain't have nothing
dat me mudder can't do
Ain't have nothing
dat me mudder can't do

Mek me tell you

* **fufu** – a type of dough
* **calaloo** – a tropical plant

Grace Nichols

- Write another verse for the poem.

Notice that the verses get longer and longer.

Teachers' note Introduce the activity by giving the children time to read the poem to themselves, and then asking them what they can tell from it about the poet, her background and culture. Revise the term 'monologue' and ask the children how they can tell that this is a monologue (it is spoken by one person, and written in the first person).

Developing Literacy
Poetry Year 6
© A & C Black

Verbs with verve

- **Re-write these lines from poems. Replace the words in bold type with a verb from the notepad.**

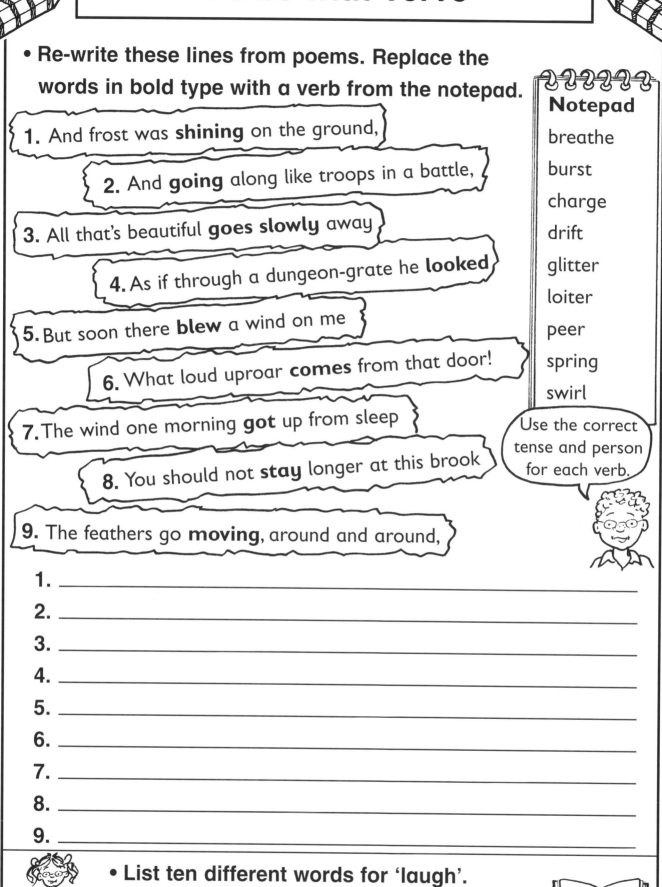

1. And frost was **shining** on the ground,

2. And **going** along like troops in a battle,

3. All that's beautiful **goes slowly** away

4. As if through a dungeon-grate he **looked**

5. But soon there **blew** a wind on me

6. What loud uproar **comes** from that door!

7. The wind one morning **got** up from sleep

8. You should not **stay** longer at this brook

9. The feathers go **moving**, around and around,

Notepad

breathe
burst
charge
drift
glitter
loiter
peer
spring
swirl

Use the correct tense and person for each verb.

1. _____
2. _____
3. _____
4. _____
5. _____
6. _____
7. _____
8. _____
9. _____

Now try this!

- **List ten different words for 'laugh'. Describe the type of laugh which each word suggests.**

Use a thesaurus.

Teachers' note Introduce the activity by reading a poem containing verbs which create a vivid impression of the actions portrayed: for example, *From a Railway Carriage* by Robert Louis Stevenson, *Goblin Market* by Christina Rossetti or *The Cataract of Lodore* by Robert Southey.

Developing Literacy
Poetry Year 6
© A & C Black

Adverbs alive

• **Underline the adverbs in the poem.**

Use a dictionary.

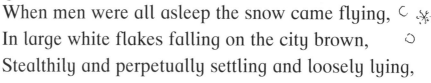

When men were all asleep the snow came flying,
In large white flakes falling on the city brown,
Stealthily and perpetually settling and loosely lying,
   Hushing the latest traffic of the drowsy town:
Deadening, muffling, stifling its murmurs failing;
Lazily and incessantly floating down and down:
   Silently sifting and veiling road, roof and railing:
Hiding difference, making unevenness even.
Into angles and crevices softly drifting and sailing.

from *London Snow* by Robert Bridges

• **Write the adverbs next to their meanings.**

Meaning	Adverb
secretly	
without force	
without stopping	

Meaning	Adverb
not fixed to the ground	
without a sound	

• **Read the poem aloud. Listen to the sounds of the adverbs.**

• **Complete the 'sound effects' chart.**

Sound effect	Adverb
alliteration	
assonance (same vowel sound)	

Now try this!

• **Describe the scene which the poem creates.**

Write sentences about what you can see, hear and feel, and about the atmosphere in the town.

Teachers' note If necessary, revise the formation and function of adverbs. Read the poem aloud and ask the children for their first impressions - even if they do not know the meanings of all the words - just from the sound of the poem and from the words whose meanings they know.

Developing Literacy
Poetry Year 6
© A & C Black

A house awakes

- List the events which happen in and around a house in the morning.
- Write words and phrases to personify the house.

Events	Personification	Useful words
curtains drawn back	windows open their eyes	arms blink cough dozing feet gargle groan hunched lazy mouth nose nosy rise shivering sing sneeze snore stare swallow teeth throat tongue wave

- Use your notes to write a list poem about a house in the morning. Use personification.

- List the events of a house at night. Personify the events.

Teachers' note Introduce personification by reading poems which personify non-living things: for example, *December* (Robert Southey), *The Wind Tapped Like a Tired Man* (Emily Dickinson), *City Jungle* (Pie Corbett), *The Wind in a Frolic* (William Howitt), *Your Friend the Sun* (Roger McGough) or *The Wind and the Moon* (George MacDonald).

Developing Literacy
Poetry Year 6
© A & C Black

Figurative language

- **This poem uses** figurative language **– similes and comparisons, metaphors and personification.**

What way does the Wind come? What way does he go?
He rides over the water, and over the snow,
Through wood and through vale; and o'er rocky height,
Which the goat cannot climb, takes his sounding flight …

He will suddenly stop in a cunning nook,
And rings a sharp 'larum; but, if you should look,
There's nothing to see but a cushion of snow
Round as a pillow, and whiter than milk,
And softer than if it were covered with silk …

Hark! over the roof he makes a pause,
And growls as if he would fix his claws
Right in the slates, and with a huge rattle
Drive them down, like men in a battle.

from *Address to a Child during a Boisterous Winter Evening* by Dorothy Wordsworth

- **Fill in a chart like this using examples from the poem.**

Similes and comparisons	Metaphors	Personification

- **How does the poet describe the character of the wind in each verse?**

Explain your answer using words from the poem.

Teachers' note The children will probably need to revise simile and metaphor (and, if they have not recently completed page 17, personification).

Developing Literacy
Poetry Year 6
© A & C Black

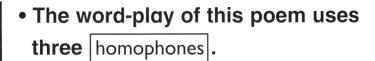

Word-play

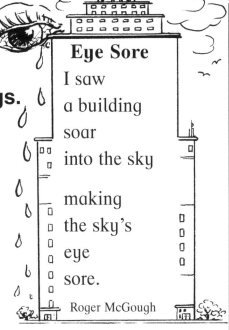

Eye Sore

I saw
a building
soar
into the sky

making
the sky's
eye
sore.

Roger McGough

- **The word-play of this poem uses three** homophones .

- **List the homophones and their meanings.**

  1. _____ _____
     _____

  2. _____ _____
     _____

  3. _____ _____
     _____

- **What two meanings does the title of the poem have?**

  1. _____
  2. _____

- **What is the poet saying about this building (and perhaps about others)?**

  _____

Now try this!

- **Write the meanings of the homophones below.**

right	stair	fair	praise
rite	stare	fare	prays
write	stir	fir	preys

vain	road	poor	rain
vane	rode	pore	reign
vein	rowed	pour	rein

- **Write sentences to link each set of homophones.**

  Example: It was her **right** to **write** about the **rite**.

Teachers' note Introduce the activity by reading other poems which feature word-play, especially by Roger McGough, Michael Rosen and Brian Patten. For the extension activity, encourage the children to make notes of any ideas they have about links between the homophones and to talk to a partner about their ideas.

Developing Literacy
Poetry Year 6
© A & C Black

Inventing words

Gerard Manley Hopkins made up words in his poems and combined words in new ways.

Inversnaid

This darksome burn, horseback brown,
His rollrock highroad roaring down,
In coop and in comb the fleece of his foam
Flutes and low to the lake falls home.

A windpuff-bonnet of fawn-froth
Turns and twindles over the broth
Of a pool so pitchblack, fell-frowning,
It rounds and rounds Despair to drowning.

Degged with dew, dappled with dew
Are the groins of the braes that the brook treads through,
Wiry heathpacks, flitches of fern,
And the beadbonny ash that sits over the burn.

What would the world be, once bereft
Of wet and of wildness? Let them be left,
O let them be left, wildness and wet;
Long live the weeds and the wilderness yet.

Gerard Manley Hopkins

- **Underline any words whose meaning you do not know.**
- **Look up these words in a dictionary. Write the meanings of those you can find.**

Use a dictionary.

- **Copy and complete the chart.**

Words made by combining words		Words used in new ways		Invented words	
Word	Meaning	Word	Meaning	Word	Meaning

Now try this!

- **Write about a place you know.**
Use some of your own made up words.

Teachers' note Discuss some of the words the children might not have met before, such as 'darksome': what do they think it means? What impression do they have of Inversnaid? They should notice the wetness, thick undergrowth of ferns and heather and the wildness. Ask what the poet is saying about wild, uncultivated areas like Inversnaid.

**Developing Literacy
Poetry Year 6
© A & C Black**

Kennings

Kenning is an old Norse term. It is a poetic phrase that is used instead of the name for something.

'husband' is from 'hus-bondi' (house farmer)

'mole' is from 'molde-warp' (earth thrower)

- **Write the kennings next to their meanings.**

  1. battle _____

  2. body _____

  3. dragon _____

  4. king _____

  5. sea _____

  6. ship _____

  7. sun _____

  8. vocabulary _____

  9. underground den or lair _____

  10. army of brave warriors _____

Kennings

bone-house	earth-hall
fire-lizard	fish-home
hero-train	ring-giver
sword-storm	wave-swimmer
word-hoard	world-candle

- **Write the modern kennings which mean:**

  11. a very tall building

  s_____

  12. a frame on which clothes are dried

  c_____ h_____

  13. a person who marries someone for his or her money

  g_____-d_____

  14. someone who drives stolen cars for fun

  j_____

- **Make up four other kennings. Give them to a friend to work out their meanings.**

Teachers' note Give examples of poetic kennings: for example, 'wave-steed' for 'ship' and 'battle-light' for 'sword', and explain that poets used kennings to express ideas and feelings and not just to describe things or make up names for them. You could read parts of the poem *Beowulf*, pointing out the many different kennings used to refer to Beowulf himself.

Developing Literacy
Poetry Year 6
© A & C Black

Nonsense words

- **Look for the nonsense words in the poem. From which words are they made up?**
- **Fill in the chart.**

Nonsense word	Made from

Eletelephony

Once there was an elephant,
Who tried to use the telephant –
No! No! I mean the elephone
Who tried to use the telephone –
(Dear me! I am not certain quite
That even now I've got it right.)

Howe'er it was, he got his trunk
Entangled in the telephunk;
The more he tried to get it free,
The louder buzzed the telephee –
(I fear I'd better drop the song
Of elephop and telephong!)

Laura E. Richards

- **Re-write the poem, changing the nonsense words so that they make sense.**

What was the poet pretending she couldn't say?

_____
_____
_____
_____
_____
_____

_____
_____
_____
_____
_____
_____

Now try this!

- **Read both versions of the poem aloud. Which is easier to read? Why? Which sounds funnier? Why?**

Teachers' note It will be useful to revise tongue-twisters before the children begin this activity. Read the poem to them and ask them how it differs from simple tongue-twisters such as *She Sells Seashells* and *Betty Botter Bought some Butter*. It is more complex, combining alliteration and rhyme as well as creating visual humour of the elephant's trunk caught in the telephone flex.

Developing Literacy
Poetry Year 6
© A & C Black

The unknown

- **The boys in the poem do not see the Snitterjipe properly.**
- **Which parts of it do they see?**

_____

_____

_____

_____

- **What do they feel?**

_____

_____

- **What do they hear?**

_____

_____

- **What feeling is created in the poem?**

_____

- **List the words which create this feeling.**

_____

_____

_____

_____

The Snitterjipe

In mellow orchards, rich and ripe,
Is found the luminous Snitterjipe.
Bad boys who climb the bulging trees
Feel his sharp breath about their knees;
His trembling whiskers tickle so,
They squeak and squeak till they let go.
They hear his far-from-friendly bark;
They see his eyeballs in the dark
Shining and shifting in their sockets
As round and as big as pears in pockets.
They feel his hot and wrinkly hide;
They see his nostrils flaming wide,
His tapering teeth, his jutting jaws,
His tongue, his tail, his twenty claws.
His hairy shadow in the moon,
It makes them sweat, it makes them swoon;
And as they climb the orchard wall
They let their pilfered apples fall.
The Snitterjipe suspends pursuit
And falls upon the fallen fruit;
And while they flee the monster fierce,
Apples, not boys, his talons pierce.
With thumping hearts they hear him munch –
Six apples at a time he'll crunch.
At length he falls asleep, and they
On tiptoe take their homeward way.
But long before the blackbirds pipe
To welcome the day, the Snitterjipe
Has fled afar, and on the green
Only his fearsome prints are seen.

James Reeves

- **Explain how the poet makes the Snitterjipe seem mysterious.**

Teachers' note Before reading the poem ask the children what 'The Snitterjipe' might be. Do they expect the poem to be funny or serious? Why? After reading the poem ask them if their predictions were right. Note that nonsense words are used not to create humour but to create an air of mystery: no one knows what the Snitterjipe is.

**Developing Literacy
Poetry Year 6
© A & C Black**

Atmosphere: 1

- **Describe the impressions the poet creates. Write in the boxes.**

What is the weather like?	**What is the mood?**

Noon

The midday hour of twelve the clock counts o'er,
   A sultry stillness lulls the air asleep;
The very buzz of flies is heard no more,
   Nor faintest wrinkles o'er the waters creep.
Like one large sheet of glass the pool does shine,
   Reflecting in its face the burnt sunbeam:
The very fish their sturting* play decline,
   Seeking the willow shadows 'side the stream.
And, where the hawthorn branches o'er the pool,
   The little bird, forsaking song and nest,
Flutters on dripping twigs his limbs to cool,
   And splashes in the stream his burning breast.
Oh, free from thunder, for a sudden shower,
   To cherish nature in this noonday hour!

John Clare

What does the bird long for?

What are all the creatures of the pool doing?

* **sturting** – attacking, darting about.

- **Describe what your body would feel like if you were in the place in the poem.** _____

_____

- **What would you feel like doing, and why?**

_____

- **Explain the contrast which emphasises the oppressive heat described in the poem.**

Teachers' note Read the poem aloud and ask the children what season and what time of day are being described. Is the atmosphere lively or still, fresh or sluggish? How can they tell? Model the answer to the first question, discussing the connotations of words such as 'sultry' and 'lulls' and the mood created by the alliteration in 'sultry stillness'.

Developing Literacy
Poetry Year 6
© A & C Black

Atmosphere: 2

Vitaï Lampada

There's a breathless hush in the Close tonight –
　　Ten to make and the match to win –
A bumping pitch and a blinding light,
　　An hour to play and the last man in.
And it's not for the sake of a ribboned coat,
　　Or the selfish hope of a season's fame,
But his Captain's hand on his shoulder smote –
　　"Play up! play up! and play the game!"

Henry Newbolt

- **What kind of atmosphere does the first line of the poem create?**

_____
_____
_____

- **Describe what the poem is about.**

_____
_____
_____
_____
_____

What has been going on and what is about to happen?

- **Explain why there is a 'breathless hush'.**

_____
_____
_____
_____

- **How do you feel by the end of the poem, and why?**

Think of the atmosphere which has been built up.

_____
_____
_____

- **What do you hope will happen?**

_____

- **Make up a poem about a sport you have watched. Create as much suspense as you can.**

Teachers' note The children should first have completed page 24. Ask them what similarities they notice between the atmospheres of this and *Noon*. What differences are there? In which poem is there a feeling that something is about to happen? Which words create this feeling? Point out the air of expectation created by the words 'breathless hush'.

Developing Literacy
Poetry Year 6
© A & C Black

Rhythm and rhyme: 1

- **Tick all the words which describe the poem.**

Speed
slow

fast

Rhythm
smooth

jerky

ambling

running

skipping

galloping

Atmosphere
peaceful

aggressive

tense

exciting

Leisure

What is this life if, full of care,
We have no time to stand and stare.

No time to stand beneath the boughs
And stare as long as sheep or cows.

No time to see, when woods we pass,
Where squirrels hide their nuts in grass.

No time to see, in broad daylight,
Streams full of stars like skies at night.

No time to turn at Beauty's glance,
And watch her feet, how they can dance.

No time to wait till her mouth can
Enrich that smile her eyes began.

A poor life this if, full of care,
We have no time to stand and stare.

W. H. Davies

- **Write the number of syllables in each line in the boxes.**
- **What do you notice?** _____
- **Underline the rhymes in different colours.**
  What do you notice? _____

Now try this!

- **How do the speed, rhythm and rhyme of the poem help to communicate its message?**

Teachers' note Ask the children to read the poem silently. Invite one of them to read it aloud while the others listen and comment on whether the speed and rhythm match the way in which they think it should be read. Discuss the ways in which the speed and rhythm of the poem reflect its subject. Ask the children what the poem's message is.

Developing Literacy
Poetry Year 6
© A & C Black

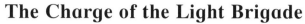

The Charge of the Light Brigade

Half a league, half a league,
Half a league onward,
All in the valley of Death
 Rode the six hundred.
 "Forward the Light Brigade!
Charge for the guns!" he said.
Into the valley of Death
 Rode the six hundred.

"Forward the Light Brigade!"
Was there a man dismayed?
Not though the soldier knew
 Some one had blundered.
Theirs not to make reply,
Theirs not to reason why,
Theirs but to do and die.
Into the valley of Death
 Rode the six hundred.

Cannon to right of them,
Cannon to left of them,
Cannon in front of them
 Volleyed and thundered;
Stormed at with shot and shell,
Boldly they rode and well,
Into the jaws of Death,
Into the mouth of Hell
 Rode the six hundred.

Flashed all the sabres bare,
Flashed as they turned in air
Sabring the gunners there,
Charging an army, while
 All the world wondered:
Plunged in the battery-smoke
Right through the line they broke;
Cossack and Russian
Reeled from the sabre-stroke
 Shattered and sundered.
Then they rode back, but not,
 Not the six hundred.

Cannon to right of them,
Cannon to left of them,
Cannon behind them
 Volleyed and thundered;
Stormed at with shot and shell,
While horse and hero fell,
They that had fought so well
Came through the jaws of Death,
Back from the mouth of Hell,
All that was left of them,
 Left of the six hundred.

When can their glory fade?
O the wild charge they made!
 All the world wondered.
Honour the charge they made!
Honour the Light Brigade,
 Noble six hundred!

Alfred, Lord Tennyson

Teachers' note Ask the children to describe the picture the poem creates for them. They could give a summary of the story of the poem and comment on the way in which the poem's rhythm reflects the action which is happening in it. See also page 28.

Developing Literacy
Poetry Year 6
© A & C Black

Rhythm and rhyme: 3

- **Read** *The Charge of the Light Brigade.*

  What do the speed and rhythm of the poem remind you of?

  _____

  Which repeated words help to create this rhythm?

  _____

  _____

  _____

  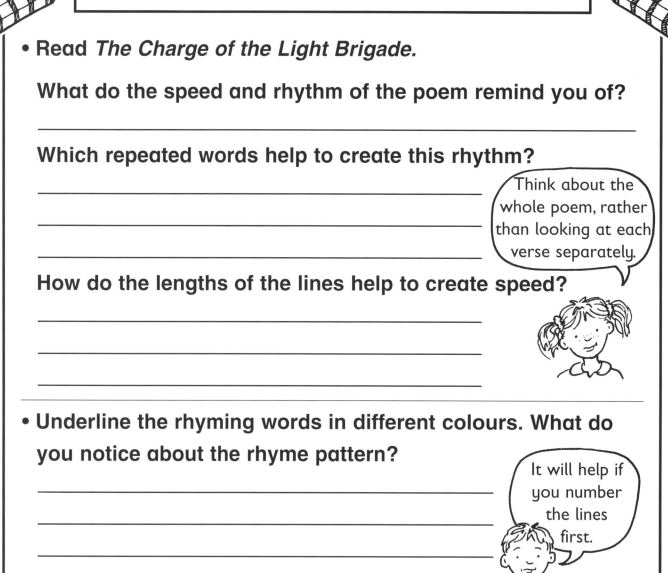

  Think about the whole poem, rather than looking at each verse separately.

  How do the lengths of the lines help to create speed?

  _____

  _____

  _____

- **Underline the rhyming words in different colours. What do you notice about the rhyme pattern?**

  _____

  _____

  _____

  _____

  It will help if you number the lines first.

- **In verses 1 to 5 there is a change of rhythm. Draw a line to show where this happens in each verse.**
  How does the rhyme change?

  _____

Now try this!

- **Why did the poet make the change in rhythm in verses 1 to 5?**
- **What was he writing about in the first part of the verse?**
- **What was he saying in the second part?**

Think about description and opinion.

Teachers' note Use this with page 27. The children could first describe the structure of the poem; what do they notice about the lengths of the verses? They might be able to comment on the effect of this.

Developing Literacy
Poetry Year 6
© A & C Black

Assonance game: 1

This is a game for three to six players.
The aim is to collect sets of four words with assonance.

Deal clockwise.

☆ Deal four cards to each player.

☆ Put the unused cards in a pile, face down.
The player to the left of the dealer has the first turn.
On each turn, you can:

☆ **Either** put back any card you do not need at the bottom of the pile and take one card from any other player (without seeing the card). If you do this, that is the end of your turn. The player whose card you have taken picks another from the top of the pile.

☆ **Or** make one set of at least two words with assonance (use any number of your cards), or add either one or two cards to a set you have already started. Then pick up cards from the top of the pile until you have four cards altogether in your hand.

☆ Continue until all the cards are used up, including those held in players' hands.

☆ Check the words in everyone's sets for assonance.

☆ Score **2** points for a set of two, **3** for a set of three and **6** for a set of four. The winner is the player with the most points.

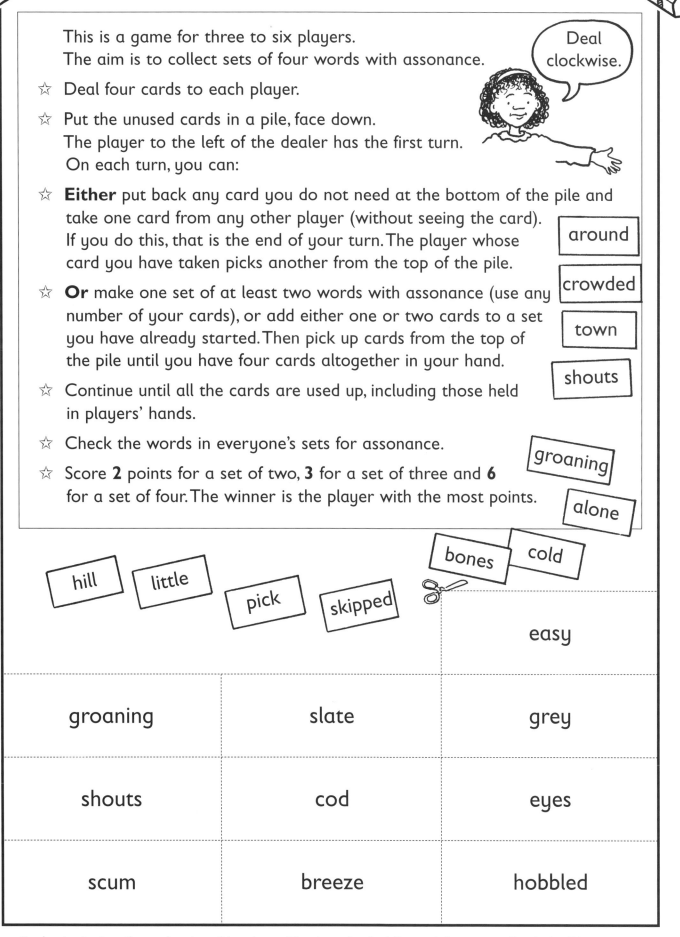

around

crowded

town

shouts

groaning

alone

bones   cold

hill   little

pick   skipped

		easy
groaning	slate	grey
shouts	cod	eyes
scum	breeze	hobbled

Teachers' note Copy the word cards on this and page 30 on to card and cut them out. Ensure that the children know what assonance means (repetition of a vowel sound: for example, through the room, cloaked in gold). Continued on page 30.

Developing Literacy
Poetry Year 6
© A & C Black

Assonance game: 2

puckered	little	alone
brooded	sky	rotting
catching	along	crowded
town	people	covered
rats	pick	night
skipped	cold	around
ugly	pale	tune
bones	soothing	fleeting
shining	doodled	vacant
pattering	battle	hill

Teachers' note Use these cards with page 29. The children could make other cards with which to play (ensure that they make four cards for each vowel sound). When they have finished the game and are adding up their points, they should check that the words in each set have assonance, by reading them aloud while the others listen.

Developing Literacy
Poetry Year 6
© A & C Black

All in a word

Well-chosen words can influence people's impressions of a person, thing, place or topic.

• Choose words from the notepad to create an impression of the word on each shape.

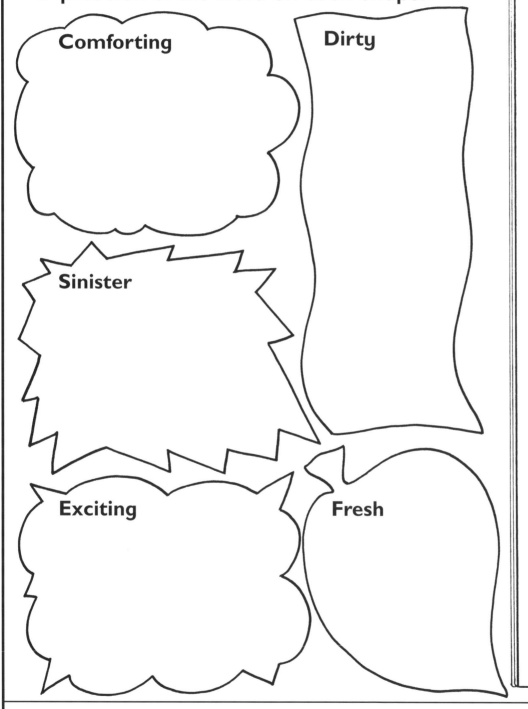

Comforting

Dirty

Sinister

Exciting

Fresh

Notepad

charging
clogged
creep
dart
dazzle
duvet
electric
fluffy
gallop
glowering
greasy
grey
grime
hero
honey
lemon
lurk
ooze
pillow
puff
pure
purr
scuttles
shower
slime
slunk
smile
soft
zest
zing

Now try this!

• Use some of the words to write about a character.
• Change the words to create a different character.

Teachers' note Model the first example. Ask the children in which shape it should be written. Ask them to explain their answers: what image does the word conjure up?

Developing Literacy
Poetry Year 6
© A & C Black

Free verse

Free verse does not follow any pattern of rhyme, rhythm or verse structure.

- **Look for rhyme in the poem. What do you notice?**

  _____

  _____

- **Listen to the rhythm of the poem. What movement is it like?**

  _____

- **What is the person in the poem doing?**

  _____

Song of the Street
In brick-grey emptiness
under the moon's sickle
I walk.
No life,
no sound,
not a withering leaf,
not a flickering straw.
Nothing
but I
in brick-grey emptiness
under the moon's sickle.
And nothing exists but me.

Steinn Steinarr
(translated by Sigurour A. Magnússon)

- **Explain how the rhythm reflects what he is doing.**

  _____

  _____

- **List the negative words in the poem.**

  _____

- **Describe the effect of these words.**

  _____

  _____

  _____

- **Describe the mood the poet creates. Give evidence from the poem.**

Teachers' note The children will notice that there is no rhyme in the poem and, although its rhythm is neither repetitive nor regular, it is nonetheless a discernible rhythm. The children could tap this rhythm on a table top as they read the poem silently. Ask them what it brings to mind.

**Developing Literacy
Poetry Year 6
© A & C Black**

Now try this!

32

Haiku

- **Read the** haiku .

Ice on the front step –
two men slip as they bring in
a new fridge freezer.

Patricia V. Dawson

→ the scene

→ what happens
and when

- **Count the syllables.**

Line 1	Line 2	Line 3	Total

- **A haiku is usually about nature. What is described in this haiku?** _____

_____

- **Make up your own haiku.**
  The first line has been completed.

Write each syllable in a separate box.

A	flurr	y	of	wind

← the scene
(something to do
with nature)

← what happens
and when, where,
why or how

- **Make up a haiku for each season of the year.**

Jot down some ideas first.

Teachers' note Revise syllables. Encourage the children to read other haiku and to count the syllables in each line. They should make jottings about what might happen in a flurry of wind, use a thesaurus to find alternative descriptive words and try out and adjust their ideas until they have the right number of syllables in each line.

**Developing Literacy
Poetry Year 6
© A & C Black**

Haiku day

Make notes about the events of a day.
- Use them to write a haiku diary.

Write each syllable in a separate box.

Event 1

← the scene

← what happens, and when, where, why or how

Event 2

Remember, a haiku should refer to nature.

Event 3

Event 4

Use a dictionary.

Event 5

Use a thesaurus.

- **Re-read and edit your haiku diary.**
Make a 'polished' copy of it.

Count the syllables.

Teachers' note The children should first have completed page 33. They could make jottings about the effects of nature: for example, what people wear in the rain, lightning striking or illuminating things and people lazing in the sunshine. Provide thesauruses. You could make spare copies of this page on which the children can try out ideas using the syllable grids.

Developing Literacy
Poetry Year 6
© A & C Black

Tanka

A tanka usually describes a special moment in time. It has a set pattern.

- Count the syllables.

Silver Aeroplane

Silver aeroplane
Speeds across the summer sky
Leaving in its wake
Trails of vapour: white scribblings
On a page of blue paper.

John Foster

Line 1	Line 2	Line 3	Line 4	Line 5

- List six subjects for tankas.

1. _____
2. _____
3. _____
4. _____
5. _____
6. _____

The subjects might happen again and again, but they'll never be identical: like a rainbow, or a cat leaping on to a high wall.

- Make notes about something you have observed which would be a good subject for a tanka.

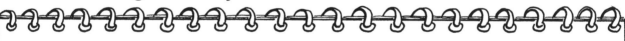

Think of comparisons, similes, metaphors and figurative language.

Now try this!

- Use your notes to write a tanka.

_____
_____
_____
_____
_____

Teachers' note Read the poem aloud to the children before providing them with a copy of it, and ask them if they know what kind of poem it is. It might be useful to revise the structure of the tanka. Discuss the nature of the subject matter, pointing out that the trail of an aeroplane is something which lasts only a short time.

Developing Literacy Poetry Year 6 © A & C Black

Wishing cinquains

- **Read the** cinquain.
- **List three wishes of your own.**

  1. _____

     _____

  2. _____

     _____

  3. _____

     _____

I wish

I wish
The answers to
Maths questions and spellings
Floated in the air to be caught
In nets.

Make notes about your ideas.

- **Plan a cinquain about one of your wishes.**

- **Write your cinquain here.**

  1. _____ 2

  2. _____ 4

  3. _____ 6

  4. _____ 8

  5. _____ 2

Check that each line has the correct number of syllables.

- **Edit and revise your cinquain.**
- **Make a 'polished' copy for a class anthology.**

Teachers' note Read the cinquain aloud and then ask the children to read it silently, counting the syllables in each line. Ask them what they notice about the structure and rhythm, and point out that cinquains do not usually rhyme.

Developing Literacy
Poetry Year 6
© A & C Black

36

What am I?

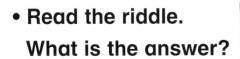

I am the Shame beneath a Carpet

I am the shame beneath a carpet.
No one comes to sweep me off my feet.

Abandoned rooms and unread books collect me.
Sometimes I dance like particles of light.

My legions thicken on each window pane,
A gathering of dusk, perpetual gloom,

And when at last the house has fallen,
I am the cloud left hanging in the air.

John Mole

- **Read the riddle. What is the answer?**

_____

- **In verse 3 which word is almost the same as the answer?**

_____

- **Explain the play on meanings in the underlined words.**

_____

_____

- **Circle the** [idioms] **in verses 1 and 4.**

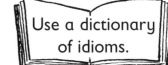

Use a dictionary of idioms.

- **Match the titles of these riddle poems to their subjects. Write the answers on the chart.**

1. I am *Lost in a Haystack.*   **a.** egg

2. I am the *Old Idea Blown Away.*   **b.** cobweb

3. I am the *Material of a Hard Heart.* **c.** stone

4. I am the *Humiliation Left on a Face.* **d.** needle

Title	Subject
1	
2	
3	
4	

Now try this!

- **Make notes for your own riddle poem about an everyday item. Write clues to help the reader to work out the answer.**

Try to use idioms in your poem.

Teachers' note Introduce the activity by reading other riddles with the children. Ask the children what they notice about the structure of a riddle and in which person it is usually written. They will need access to a dictionary of idioms: for example, *The Penguin Dictionary of English Idioms.*

Developing Literacy
Poetry Year 6
© A & C Black

37

Parody

A parody is a humorous poem or story based on another poem or story.

- **The Owl and the Astronaut** is based on which poem?

_____

_____

- **Circle the parts which are exactly the same as the original poem.**

- **List the words that have changed. Write what they originally said.**

_____

_____

_____

_____

_____

_____

The Owl and the Astronaut

The owl and the astronaut
Sailed through space
In their intergalactic ship.
They kept hunger at bay
With three pills a day
And drank through a protein drip.
The owl dreamed of mince
And slices of quince
And remarked how life had gone flat;
"It may be all right
To fly faster than light
But I preferred the boat and the cat."

Gareth Owen

- **Make notes for another parody.**

Choose another old poem and bring it up to date.

- **Write your poem. Check that it has the same rhythm as the original.**

Teachers' note Provide a copy of *The Owl and the Pussy-Cat* by Edward Lear with which the children can compare this poem. (It can be found in many anthologies, including *The Oxford Book of Children's Verse*.) They could collaborate on a class parody of the complete poem, each group contributing a verse.

Developing Literacy
Poetry Year 6
© A & C Black

Limerick rhyme patterns

- **Underline the rhymes in red.**
- **Underline repeated words in blue.**

 These limericks are by Edward Lear.

There was an Old Person of Dutton
Whose head was as small as a button,
   So, to make it look big,
   He purchased a wig,
And rapidly rushed about Dutton.

There was a Young Girl of Majorca,
Whose aunt was a very fast walker;
   She walked seventy miles,
   And leaped fifteen stiles,
Which astonished that Girl of Majorca.

- **Fill in the gaps in these limericks.**

There was an Old Man of Torquay

Who spent ten pounds on a ＿＿＿＿＿＿

He ＿＿＿＿＿＿＿＿＿＿＿＿＿＿＿＿＿＿＿

＿＿＿＿＿＿＿＿＿＿＿＿＿＿＿＿＿＿＿＿＿＿＿

＿＿＿＿＿＿＿＿＿＿＿＿＿＿＿＿＿＿＿＿＿＿＿

There was a Young Lady from France

＿＿＿＿＿＿＿＿＿＿＿＿＿＿＿＿＿＿＿＿＿＿＿

＿＿＿＿＿＿＿＿＿＿＿＿＿＿＿＿＿＿＿＿＿＿＿

＿＿＿＿＿＿＿＿＿＿＿＿＿＿＿＿＿＿＿＿＿＿＿

＿＿＿＿＿＿＿＿＿＿＿＿＿＿＿＿＿＿＿＿＿＿＿

Useful rhyming words

away	day
flea	CD
tree	me
night	right
fight	light
dance	prance
chance	ease
knees	please
jig	wig

- **List four places and four words which rhyme with them. Use your words to make other limericks.**

Teachers' note The children could prepare for this activity by bringing in examples of limericks. Ask them how they can distinguish a limerick from any other kind of poem and discuss the number of lines, the rhythm and the rhyme pattern.

**Developing Literacy
Poetry Year 6
© A & C Black**

Sounds funny: 1

- **Circle the names of vegetables, fruits and other plants in this poem. In the outlines, write the words they have replaced.**

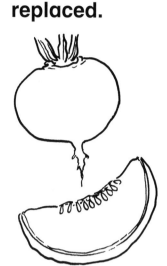

care at

The Greengrocer's Love Song

Do you (carrot) all for me?
My heart beets for you.
With your turnip nose
And your radish face
You are a peach.
If we canteloupe
Lettuce marry.
Weed make a swell pear.

Anonymous

- **Replace each word in bold type with a word from the notepad.**

  The words should have similar sounds.

  Tree school playtime

  "It's not **fair** (_____)!

  I'm not **playing** (_____)!"

  "**OK** (_____), bring your **own** (_____) ball!"

  "**Will you** (_____) play with me?"

  "Well, I'll **ask** (_____) my friend to join us.

  "We shouldn't **leave** (_____) her out."

  Useful words

ash	fir
leaf	oak
plane	rowan
	willow

Now try this!

- **Write the names of foods which sound like other words.**

  For example, pizza (piece of).

- **Use them in a poem.**

Teachers' note The activity could be introduced by reading the poem aloud to the children before they have been given a copy of it. Ask them what makes it a *greengrocer's* love song. Provide them with copies of the poem and ask them if seeing the poem in writing helps them to appreciate the humour.

Developing Literacy
Poetry Year 6
© A & C Black

Sounds funny: 2

In a spoonerism the first letters of
words are swapped. It is named
after the Reverend William Spooner,
who often mixed up words in this way.

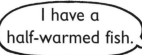

I have a
half-warmed fish.

He means a
half-formed wish.

- **Write the meanings of these spoonerisms.**

1.
It roared with
pain all day.

2.
We were muck
in the stud.

3.
He's as mean as
custard.

4.
My hobby is
beading rooks.

5.
Let sleeping logs
die.

6.
He had three
mare squeals
per day.

1.	2.	3.
4.	5.	6.

- **Make up spoonerisms for the items on the shopping list.**

a pound of meat

a can of pears

a tin of beans

jelly beans

peas and carrots

dates and figs

chick peas

wheat flakes

Now try this!

- **Make up six spoonerisms about sports and games.**

Teachers' note Read the introduction to the activity to the children, and ask them if they have
heard any examples of 'spoonerisms'. Tell them others of the Reverend Spooner's examples: 'a
well-boiled icicle' and 'a boiled sprat' and ask them if they can work out what he meant to say
('a well-oiled bicycle' and 'a spoiled brat').

Developing Literacy
Poetry Year 6
© A & C Black

Symbol fun

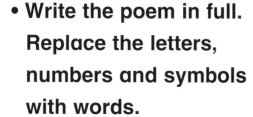

- **Write the poem in full. Replace the letters, numbers and symbols with words.**

_____

_____

_____

_____

_____

_____

_____

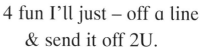

OIC

I'm in a 10der mood today
& feel poe ✔, 2;
4 fun I'll just – off a line
& send it off 2U.

I'm sorry you've been 6 so long;
Don't B disconsol8;
But bear your ills with 42de,
& they won't seem so gr8.

Anonymous

- **Use letters, numbers and symbols to write these words and phrases.**

comet _____   slapdash _____

too late _____   once _____

fortify _____   relate _____

frantic _____   tentacle _____

fortune _____   dashing _____

like a bull at a gate _____

a late starter _____

pounded _____   starvation _____

Swansea _____   acrostic _____

Iceland _____   panda _____

Useful symbols

x cross

, comma

£ pound

– dash

✔ tick

& and

• bullet

✳ star

- **Use letters, numbers and symbols to write a message for a friend to decode.**

Teachers' note Ask the children if they can give any examples of numbers used as words. They might have come across the following well-known one: 2YsUR, 2YsUB, ICUR2Ys4ME (Too wise you are, too wise you be, I see you are too wise for me).

Developing Literacy
Poetry Year 6
© A & C Black

Playing with meanings

- **Explain the humour of the words in bold type.**

A Bad Case of Fish

A **chip**-shop owner's in the **dock**
on a charge of assault and **battery**.
The **monkfish** takes the oath:
So help me **cod** …

The courtroom's packed with lost **soles**.
The **crabby** judge can't find his **plaice**
or read the prosecution's **whiting**.
And what sort of fish is a saveloy, anyway?

The young **skates** are getting bored.
They start **skateboarding** down the aisles.
The **scampi** scamper to and fro.
The eels are dancing **congers**.

But the case is cut and dried.
It's all **wrapped up**. (Just look
in the evening paper.) Next,
the **Krayfish twins** …

Philip Gross

Think of similar-sounding words, homophones and linked meanings.

Ships are found in docks.

The **dock** is where witnesses give evidence in court.

Monkfish is a

Cod sounds like

Soles

Skate

Krayfish twins
Crayfish are shellfish and the Kray twins were notorious criminals.

Chip sounds similar to ship.

Battery means harming someone physically and fish are battered before they are cooked.

Crabby

Plaice

Whiting

Scampi

Congers

Wrapped up

Teachers' note Introduce different types of word-play using the names of animals: for example, 'the cows cowered' and 'the mare coughed hoarsely'. Read the poem aloud and help the children to find the word-play in the first verse. As an extension activity the children could make up other word-plays.

Developing Literacy Poetry Year 6
© A & C Black

Analysing a poem

- **What is the subject of this poem?**

  _____

- **Which words tell you this?** _____

  _____

  _____

  _____

  _____

- **Does the cat understand what is going on?**

  _____

- **How can you tell?**

  _____

  _____

  _____

  _____

  _____

  _____

  _____

  _____

They're Fetching in Ivy and Holly

"They're fetching in ivy and holly
And putting it this way and that.
I simply can't think of the reason,"
Said Si-Si the Siamese cat.

"They're pinning up lanterns and streamers.
There's mistletoe over the door.
They've brought in a tree from the garden.
I do wish I knew what it's for.

"It's covered with little glass candles
That go on and off without stop.
They've put it to stand in a corner
And tied up a fairy on top.

"They're stringing bright cards by the dozen
And letting them hang in a row.
Some people outside in the roadway
Are singing a song in the snow.

"I saw all the children write letters
And – I'm not at all sure this was wise –
They posted each one up the chimney.
I couldn't believe my own eyes.

"What on earth, in the middle of winter,
Does the family think it is at?
Won't somebody come and tell me?"
Said Si-Si the Siamese cat.

Charles Causley

- **What is the poet saying about the things people do at Christmas?**
- **Explain how the poet expresses his views about Christmas preparations.**

Now try this!

Teachers' note Ask the children if they find the poem funny, and why. What explanations would they give to the cat? Let them consider if these explanations make sense in relation to the Christian celebration of Christmas. What do they notice?

Developing Literacy Poetry Year 6
© A & C Black

Layers of meaning

• **Write a summary of what happens in the poem.**

In This City

In this city, perhaps a street.
In this street, perhaps a house.
In this house, perhaps a room.
And in this room a woman sitting,
Sitting in the darkness, sitting and crying
For someone who has just gone through the door
And who has just switched off the light
Forgetting she was there.

Alan Brownjohn

_____

_____

_____

_____

_____

_____

_____

• **Why is the woman crying?**

Think about just that one occasion.

_____

_____

_____

• **You have explained the** literal meaning **of the poem. What deeper meaning does it have?**

_____

_____

_____

Is that the only time the woman cried? Is there another reason for her to be sad?

_____

_____

_____

_____

_____

_____

• **Describe how the poet creates the atmosphere of loneliness.**

Now try this!

Teachers' note Read the poem with the children and ask them to describe the picture they imagine and the feelings the poem evokes in them. Ask them to explain how the poet creates that picture and evokes that feeling.

Developing Literacy
Poetry Year 6
© A & C Black

Linked by a letter

- **Write a summary of what each poem says.**

There was a young man who said, 'God
Must think it exceedingly odd
   If he finds that this tree
   Continues to be
When there's no one about in the Quad.

_____

_____

_____

_____

_____

_____

_____

_____

_____

_____

_____

Dear Sir,
Your astonishment's odd:
I am always about in the Quad.
   And that's why the tree
   Will continue to be,
   Since observed by
Yours faithfully,
God.

- **Choose one of the topics in the box.**
  Make notes for a letter poem.

> bullies
> ghosts
> school dinners
> school uniform

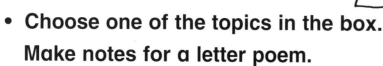

- **Write a reply to your letter poem.**

Make notes first
to help you.

Now try this!

- **Re-read and edit your poems.**
  Write 'polished' versions.

Teachers' note Explain that the first poem was written by an early twentieth-century theologian named Ronald Knox to mock the theory of Bishop George Berkeley (1685–1753), that things stopped existing if no one was observing them. The second poem was published in the *Times* newspaper as an anonymous reply.

**Developing Literacy
Poetry Year 6
© A & C Black**

A poem from the past

• **This poem was written in Elizabethan times. Read the poem aloud. Try to work out the meanings of unfamiliar words.**

What modern words do the old words sound like?

Then came the *Autumne* all in yellow clad,
As though he joyed in his plentious store,
Laden with fruits that made him laugh, full glad
That he had banisht hunger, which to-fore
Had by the belly oft him pinched sore.
Upon his head a wreath that was enrold
With eares of corne of every sort he bore:
And in his hand a sickle he did holde,
To reape the ripened fruits the which the earth had yold.

from *Mutabilitie*, part of *The Faerie Queene* by Edmund Spenser

Find out what 'Mutabilitie' means.

• **Fill in the chart.**

Elizabethan language			
Changed spellings		**Words used differently or no longer used**	
Word	Meaning	Word	Meaning
Autumne	Autumn	joyed in	enjoyed

Now try this!

• **Give examples of past tenses used in the poem which were formed differently. Write them in modern English.**
• **Give two examples of word-order which are different from modern English. Explain the differences.**

Teachers' note Read the poem aloud and ask the children to identify the subject-matter. Ask them to give a brief summary of how the poet depicts autumn. They could also comment on the use of comparison, metaphor, figurative language and personification. Encourage them to work out the meanings of the unfamiliar words from their contexts.

Developing Literacy
Poetry Year 6
© A & C Black

A poet's style

Poet _____   Date(s) _____

Place of birth _____

Titles of poems read, and subjects	Poet's views
	How I can tell

Poetic forms used	**Poetic devices used**
Free verse, haiku, tanka, limerick, monologue…	Metaphor, simile, figurative language, kenning…

How the poet uses sound

Rhythm, rhyme, half-rhyme, assonance, alliteration, onomatopoeia…

Teachers' note If necessary, enlarge the page to A3. It could be used as the basis for a class activity on the same poet (perhaps one of those whose work appears in this book), or for the children to write about a poet of their choice. They should explain their answers using examples.

Developing Literacy Poetry Year 6 © A & C Black